The BATHROOM TRIVIA COMPANION

·

by

Jack Kreismer

RED-LETTER PRESS, INC.
Saddle River, New Jersey

Red-Letter Press, Inc.
P.O. Box 393
Saddle River, NJ 07458

www.Red-LetterPress.com

ACKNOWLEDGMENTS

"HEAD" CONTRIBUTOR AND
LIFE OF THE POTTY:
Russ Edwards

•

EDITORIAL:
Jeff Kreismer

•

BOOK DESIGN & TYPOGRAPHY:
Jeff Kreismer

•

COVER ART:
Cliff Behum

•

RESEARCH & DEVELOPMENT:
Kobus Reyneke
Rory Tomlinson

First Things First

Lt. Thomas Selfridge, 26, was the first person killed in a plane crash, in 1908. Orville Wright was the pilot.

• •

Cover to cover: The first cover of "TV Guide" in 1953 showed Lucille Ball and her newborn son. Eddie Mathews was on the cover of "Sports Illustrated" in 1954, John Lennon was on "Rolling Stone" in 1967, and Mia Farrow was featured on "People" in 1974.

• •

Willard Scott was the first Ronald McDonald, in 1963. The future "Today Show" weatherman was reportedly fired for being too fat.

• •

President Rutherford B. Hayes had the first telephone put in the White House in 1877. It was installed by Alexander Graham Bell.

• •

The first U.S. president to use email was Ronald Reagan.

Men who consistently leave the toilet seat up secretly want women to get up to go to the bathroom in the middle of the night and fall in.
-Rita Rudner

A MATTER OF SECONDS

1. Statistics show that Cinco De Mayo is the biggest day for Americans to eat avocados. Can you tackle the second biggest avocado-eating occasion?

2. Who is second to Barry Bonds on Major League Baseball's all-time home run list?

3. Delaware became the first state in the U.S. Which state was second?

4. Before 1900, the Eiffel Tower, at 984 feet, was the world's tallest building. What was second?

5. What is second to the Nile (4,145 miles) as the world's longest river?

ANSWERS: 1.Super Bowl Sunday 2.Hank Aaron, with 755 homers (Bonds hit 762) 3.Pennsylvania 4.The Washington Monument- 555 feet 5.The Amazon (4,007 miles)

Abraham Lincoln and Charles Darwin were born on the exact same day, February 12, 1809.

•

A trip around the bases on a baseball diamond is the exact same distance as running the length of a football field, including the end zones- 360 feet.

•

The glabella is the space between your eyebrows.

•

At one time, the pharmaceutical company Bayer held the trademark for the word "heroin" and sold the drug as a cough and headache remedy.

•

In 1881, the United States had three different presidents: Rutherford B. Hayes, James Garfield, and Chester A. Arthur.

•

Squid is the number one pizza topping in Japan.

If I want to be alone, some place I can write, I can read, I can pray, I can cry, I can do whatever I want - I go to the bathroom.

-Alicia Keys

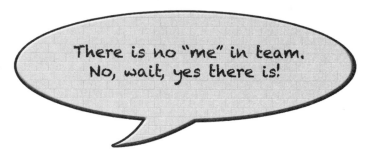

There is no "me" in team.
No, wait, yes there is!

A couple of guys with the "right stuff" participated together in U.S. bombing missions over Korea. Astronaut John Glenn and baseball Hall of Famer Ted Williams were co-pilots.

•

On sunny days, the Eiffel Tower leans slightly toward the shade.

•

Conventional wisdom says that people use DVRs to skip ads, but Nielsen surveys say that 45 percent of all recorded commercials are still viewed.

•

Francis Galton developed fingerprinting as a means for identification. Galton was Charles Darwin's cousin.

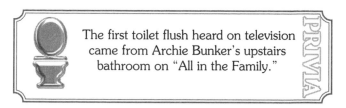

The first toilet flush heard on television came from Archie Bunker's upstairs bathroom on "All in the Family."

ALPHABET SOUP

1. E is the most often used letter of the English alphabet. What letter is second in terms of frequency?

2. A, E, H, I, K, L, M, N, O, P, U and W are of what significance in Hawaii?

3. What does S.P.E.B.S.Q.S.A. stand for?

4. What does the "J.C." in JC Penney stand for?

5. What three-letter word is the last entry in the Random House Unabridged Dictionary, Second Edition?

ANSWERS: 1.The letter T 2.They are the twelve – and only twelve – letters of the Hawaiian alphabet. 3.The Society for the Preservation and Encouragement of Barbershop Quartet Singing in America 4.C as in Cash, James Cash Penney, that is. 5.Zzz, defined as "the sound of a person snoring"

In a house where there are small children the bathroom soon takes on the appearance of the Old Curiosity Shop.
-Robert Benchley

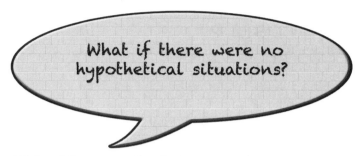

What if there were no hypothetical situations?

Mickey Mouse was the first cartoon character to receive a star on the Hollywood Walk of Fame.

•

Jimi Hendrix, believe it or not, opened for the Monkees.

•

In 1927, Morris Frank became the recipient of the first U.S. dog guide, a German Shepherd named "Buddy."

•

The "real" name of The Riddler in "Batman" is Edward Nigma (E. Nigma, get it?).

•

In writing his own tombstone, Thomas Jefferson forgot to mention that he was once President of the United States.

•

Lou Gehrig's salary in 1927, as a member of the New York Yankees' "Murderer's Row," was $8,000.

•

That hole in your shirt that you put your arm through? It's called an "armsaye."

The term "couch potato" is the legal property of Robert Armstrong, who trademarked it in 1976.

•

SpongeBob was originally going to be called SpongeBoy but the name was already in use for a mop product.

•

Only two countries in the world are spelled with the letter "x"- Luxembourg and Mexico.

•

The winner of the 1898 Boston Marathon was Ronald McDonald.

•

Brenda Lee was 13 years old when she recorded "Rockin' Around the Christmas Tree."

•

It'll take you more than thirty years to count to a billion. Try it or take our word for it.

•

Albert Einstein never learned how to drive.

At a formal dinner party, the person nearest death should always be seated closest to the bathroom.
-George Carlin

Delete 'history' and start all over again.

It's scientifically proven that the sight of red makes you hungrier than any other color.

•

To add some spice to your life, you might want to visit the Salt and Pepper Shaker Museum in Gatlinburg, Tennessee, where over 20,000 salt and pepper shakers from all over the world are on display.

•

To heave or not to heave: An area of the brain known as the bilateral vomitation center notices when our stomach is upset and makes the final decision on barfing.

•

Chandra Bahadur Dangi, born in Nepal in 1939, is the world's shortest man according to Guinness. He is 21 inches tall.

Because it was built before desegregation, the Pentagon has twice the number of toilets needed for a building of its size.

PRIVIA

Child Prodigies

Shirley Temple received an Academy Award at the age of seven.

• •

Tiger Woods was introduced to golf before the age of two by his father. He first broke 80 at the age of eight.

• •

Nadia Comaneci won 3 gold medals at the 1976 Olympics and was the first female to achieve a perfect score of 10 in gymnastics when she was 15.

• •

Willie Mosconi, "Mr. Pocket Billiards," played against professionals at the age of six.

• •

Pablo Picasso painted "Picador" at eight years old.

• •

Tatum O'Neal won the Best Supporting Actress Oscar at 10 years old for her 1973 role in "Paper Moon," making her the youngest person ever to win a regularly awarded Oscar.

For marriage to be a success, every woman and every man should have her and his own bathroom. The end.
-Catherine Zeta-Jones

Pyromaniacs wear blazers.

THINKING BIG

1. What company is nicknamed "Big Brown"?

2. Do you know the stage name of rock 'n' roll singer J.P. Richardson?

3. He's a member of the warm-blooded egg-laying vertebrate family and is seen on a popular children's television show. Name him.

4. What Triple Crown-winning racehorse was nicknamed "Big Cy"?

5. "Big Salt Lick" was the original name of what city?

ANSWERS: 1.United Parcel Service, for its fleet of brown trucks
2.Big Bopper 3.Big Bird 4.Citation 5.Nashville, Tennessee

Pepsi's red, white, and blue logo was made in the 1940s to support America's war effort.

•

A dog's nose print is as unique as a person's fingerprints.

•

Facebook engineers originally wanted to name the "Like" button the "Awesome" button.

•

When Twister was introduced by Milton Bradley in 1966, critics denounced the game as "sex in a box."

•

During the 2002 Iraqi election, Whitney Houston's "I Will Always Love You" was Saddam Hussein's campaign song.

•

You can use potato chips to start a fire.

•

The feminine for "dude" is "dudette."

I sleep with a light on in the bathroom so I can see where I'm at, because I wake up and have no clue!
-Carrie Underwood

Twitter's bird logo is named Larry, after Boston Celtics Hall of Famer Larry Bird.

•

Dave Thomas, the founder of Wendy's, became a millionaire while working at Kentucky Fried Chicken.

•

18 million other people in the world share your birthday with you.

•

In colonial America, lobster was anything but a delicacy, so cheap and plentiful that it was often served to prisoners.

•

It's been estimated that 15% to 20% of people who receive gift cards never redeem them.

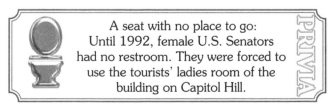

A seat with no place to go:
Until 1992, female U.S. Senators had no restroom. They were forced to use the tourists' ladies room of the building on Capitol Hill.

SEEING STARS

1. Name the television reality show based on the British series "Strictly Come Dancing."

2. What is the nickname of the flag of the Confederate States of America?

3. Do you know the Green Bay Packers quarterback who was the MVP of the first two Super Bowls?

4. What chain opened its first retail store in Seattle's Pike Place Market in 1971?

5. The Singing Cowboy has the most stars on the Hollywood Walk of Fame, five (for five different entertainment categories). Can you name him?

ANSWERS: 1."Dancing with the Stars" 2.Stars and Bars 3.Bart Starr 4.Starbucks 5.Gene Autry

I knew I was an unwanted baby when I saw that my bath toys were a toaster and a radio.

-Joan Rivers

Otto Titzling did not invent the bra no matter what Trivial Pursuit says. He's a fictional character in Wallace Reyburn's 1971 novel "Bust-Up: The Uplifting Tale of Otto Titzling and the Development of the Bra."

•

In a Sesame Street episode, Cookie Monster said that before he started eating cookies, his name was Sid.

•

Dogs can understand about a two hundred word human vocabulary, while cats comprehend only about fifty words.

•

When Oreo cookies were first made, they were mound-shaped. The name comes from the Greek word "oreo", which means "hill."

•

The 1,500 pound leatherback turtle carries a shell that is as big as a king size bed- but a lot harder to find fitted sheets for!

A snake can hear with its tongue.

•

In 1950, the town of Hot Springs, New Mexico, renamed itself Truth or Consequences in honor of the old TV game show.

•

A Slinky has 63 feet of wire.

•

Pat Sajak and David Letterman were both local TV weathermen.

•

Demi Moore was cross-eyed as a child and had corrective surgery- twice.

•

An elephant smells through its mouth, not its trunk.

•

An ant's sense of smell is just as good as a dog's.

*Basically my wife was immature.
I'd be at home in the bath and she'd
come in and sink my boats.*
-Woody Allen

There are an average of 216 noodles in a can of Campbell's Chicken Noodle Soup.

•

The human tooth has approximately fifty miles of canals in it.

•

English muffins were first made in America, Venetian blinds were invented by the Chinese, and Belgians were the first to make French fries.

•

There are no photographs that show Abraham Lincoln smiling.

•

15% of auctions are won in the last minute on eBay.

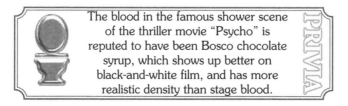

The blood in the famous shower scene of the thriller movie "Psycho" is reputed to have been Bosco chocolate syrup, which shows up better on black-and-white film, and has more realistic density than stage blood.

Q&As On Your ABCs

Q: How high would you have to count before using the letter A in a whole number?

A: One thousand

Q: When three-letter airport codes became standard, airports that had been using two letters simply added what letter?

A: X

Q: What does the Q in Q-tips stand for?

A: Quality (By the way, Q-tips were originally called Baby Gays.)

Q: Does the B in Susan B. Anthony stand for Brownell, Barbara or Bartholemew?

A: Brownell (Numismatists will be interested to know that the Susan B. Anthony dollar marked the first time a real woman appeared on U.S. currency. Others might be interested to know what a numismatist is- a coin collector.)

I worked in a health food store once. A guy came in and asked me, 'If I melt dry ice, can I take a bath without getting wet?'
-Steven Wright

Lazy People Fact
#4395738342618:
You were too lazy to read
that number.

COMMON CENTS

1. How many ridges are on a quarter?
a) 1 b) 50 c) 119 d) 1776

2. Which lasts longer in circulation, the average coin or the dollar bill?

3. What's the most amount of change you could have without being able to make change for a dollar bill?

4. Of the penny, nickel, dime and quarter, which is the only one where the "head" is facing to the right?

5. True or false? The original motto on U.S. coins was "Mind Your Business."

ANSWERS: 1.C 2.The average coin circulates for 15 to 20 years while the life span of a dollar bill is approximately 22 months according to "Forbes" magazine. 3.$1.19- Three quarters, four dimes and four pennies 4.Honest Abe Lincoln, on the penny, is the only one facing right. 5.True

Dalmatian dogs are pure white when they're born.

•

Approximately 98% of all coupons go unused.

•

Caesar salad has nothing to do with the rulers of Rome. It was first made in a Tijuana bar in the 1920s.

•

84% of cat owners are women.

•

Before "Hello" became the standard telephone greeting, folks said "Ahoy." Thomas Edison suggested the change.

•

It cost $1 for admission to Disneyland when it opened in 1955.

•

Horse racing legend Man O' War had a bad mare day when he suffered his only defeat- to a horse named Upset.

My name is only an anagram of toilets.
-T.S. Eliot

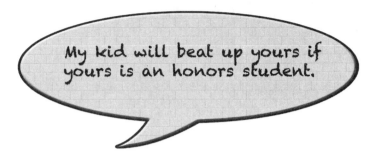

My kid will beat up yours if yours is an honors student.

The first minimum wage, instituted in the U.S. in 1938, was 25 cents an hour.

•

Tweety Pie was originally a pink canary, but censors complained that he looked naked so his color was changed to yellow.

•

Elephants can swim very well. (They just have trouble keeping their trunks up.)

•

Pepto Bismol, when introduced in 1901, was called Mixture Cholera Infantum.

•

Alligator shirts have crocodiles on them.

 The Mona Lisa was purchased in 1517 by King Francis I of France to hang in the bathroom.

Twenty Questions

1. How many people signed the Declaration of Independence?

2. How many dice are used in the game of Yahtzee?

3. Who is the last president that didn't attend college?

4. Who was Major League Baseball's first designated hitter?

5. How many zeros does a septillion have?

6. In which hand does the Statue of Liberty hold her torch?

7. You know Jorge Mario Bergoglio better by another name. What is it?

8. What is the plural of praying mantis?

You can stand up in front of a bunch of four-year-olds and just say 'toilet,' and they'll start laughing.
-Charlie Williams

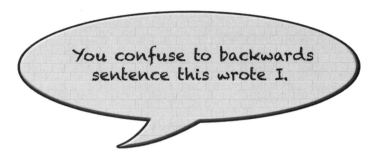

9. What job did Robert E. Lee turn down to accept command of the Confederate forces?

10. Can you name the only airline with a name composed of three consecutive letters?

11. Within a hundred pounds or so, if you wanted to steal a billion dollars in $100 bills, how much weight would you have to be prepared to carry?

12. What does "Mardi Gras" mean?

13. How many sides are there on a dodecagon?

14. Buffalo Bill Cody gave what sharpshooter the nickname "Little Sure Shot"?

15. What's the most popular first name for a U.S. president?

16. What sports Hall of Fame is located in Springfield, Massachusetts?

17. Who are Moses Horwitz, Jerome Horwitz, and Larry Feinberg?

18. True or false? Prince Charles is an avid collector of toilet seats.

19. How many pennies are in a pound?
A: 54 B: 100 C: 123 D: 181

20. Who was the originator of the military decoration known as "The Purple Heart?"

ANSWERS: 1.56 – John Hancock was the first to sign. 2.5 3.Harry S Truman 4.New York Yankee Ron Blomberg, who was walked by Red Sox pitcher, Luis Tiant, on April 6, 1973 5.24 6.Right 7.Pope Francis 8.Praying mantid 9.Lee declined command of the Union forces. He apparently felt his loyalty was to his home state of Virginia. 10.KLM 11.A billion bucks in C-notes would be some seriously heavy bread. In fact, it would weigh about 10 tons! 12.Literally translated, it means "Fat Tuesday." 13.12 14.Annie Oakley 15.James (Madison, Monroe, Polk, Buchanan, Garfield, and Carter) 16.Basketball 17.They are the three Stooges: Moe, Curley and Larry. 18.True 19.D 20.George Washington

Life unrolls like toilet paper. The closer it gets to the end, the faster it goes.

-Lorrin L. Lee

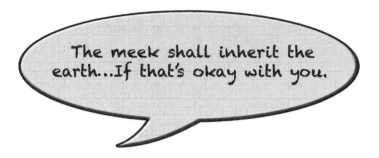

The meek shall inherit the earth...If that's okay with you.

Harry Truman's buddies had a bowling alley installed in the White House for the president's birthday in 1947.

•

Potato chips were invented in 1853 in Saratoga, New York, by George Crum.

•

Smokey Bear is the only one in America with his own zip code- 20252.

•

The second man to walk on the lunar surface was Buzz Aldrin. His mother's maiden name is Moon.

•

"Chop suey" means "odds and ends."

According to a 2013 Michigan State University study, only 5% of people wash their hands enough to kill infection and illness-causing germs after using the bathroom.

Home plate in baseball was square until 1900 when it was made five-sided to help umpires in calling balls and strikes.

•

Edgar Allan Poe often wrote his works with his cat seated on his shoulder.

•

The average American laughs fifteen times a day.

•

Guinness says the world's hardest tongue twister is this: "The sixth sick sheik's sixth sheep's sick."

•

If you suffer from polydactylism, you have more than your fair share of fingers or toes.

•

Pink lemonade was created in 1857 by Pete Conklin, who unwittingly used a bucket of water in which a circus performer had soaked his red tights.

Instead of the John, I call my bathroom the Jim... That way it sounds better when I say I go to the Jim every morning.
    -Jamie Capria

> May you run out of toilet paper when you need it most.

10 Appropriate Anagrams

Astronomer: Moon starer

Bill Gates: Gets a bill

Clint Eastwood: Old west action

David Letterman: Nerd amid late TV

Dennis Rodman: Odd in manners

Dormitory: Dirty room

Jennifer Aniston: Fine in torn jeans

Morse Code: Here come dots

Mother-in-law: Woman Hitler

Snooze alarms: Alas! No more Zs

AFFAIRS OF STATE

1. The least populous state in the U.S. is:
a) Montana b) Wyoming c) Rhode Island d) California

2. In what state is the geographic center of North America?

3. The forget-me-not is, fittingly, the state flower of ...?

4. At Four Corners, you can walk in four states within a few seconds. Can you name those states?

5. Mt. McKinley is the highest peak in the United States. In what state is it located? And, for extra credit, what was the highest peak in the U.S. before Mt. McKinley was discovered?

ANSWERS: 1.B 2.North Dakota, in Pierce County 3.Alaska 4. Arizona, Colorado, New Mexico and Utah 5.Alaska- As for the second part to that question, the highest peak before Mt. McKinley was discovered was- Mt. McKinley! It just hadn't been discovered yet.

My roommate says, 'I'm going to take a shower and shave, does anyone need to use the bathroom?' It's like some weird quiz where he reveals the answer first.

-Mitch Hedberg

My likely obituary:
"Died from not forwarding
that e-mail to 10 people."

Harrison Ford has a species of spider, Calponia harrisonfordi, named after him.

•

Albert Einstein never wore socks.

•

Jerry Seinfeld sold light bulbs by telephone.

•

It wasn't until the Civil War that specific left and right shoes were made.

•

Less than half of the single men in the U.S. who've reached the age of 35 ever get married.

When Johnny Carson hosted the "Tonight Show," he once joked about a scarcity of toilet paper during his monologue. It created a nationwide run on the product, causing a real shortage.

Jack Nicholson single-handedly rescued five drowning people from the New Jersey surf back in the 1950s.

•

One of the longest named phobias is macroxenoglossophobia - a fear of long words!

•

Diamonds are flammable - but only at temperatures higher than 1,400 degrees Fahrenheit. Talk about hot rocks!

•

Fairy tale writer Hans Christian Anderson was dyslexic. Others afflicted by dyslexia include Thomas Edison, Woodrow Wilson, Tom Cruise and Henry Winkler.

•

The largest muscle in your body is the gluteus maximus.

•

Charles Osborne owns the Guinness world record for having a case of the hiccups for the longest time- 68 years, from 1922-1990.

I refuse to go to the bathroom on an airplane because if I'm gonna die in a cartwheeling ball of flames, it is not going to be in a flying outhouse with my pants around my ankles.

-Sabrina Matthews

Why didn't Noah swat those two mosquitoes?

Heads Portland, tails Boston. In an 1844 coin toss, Portland was selected over Boston as the city name in Oregon.

•

Show me a rooster that cannot extend its neck and I'll show you a rooster that cannot crow.

•

A polar bear's skin is black.

•

Coca Cola has never been patented, because to do so, the secret formula would have to be revealed.

•

India has no less than 15 official languages.

•

According to people who watch such things, women's buttocks protrude 25% more when they wear high heels.

•

Your typical hen lays about 300 eggs per year.

PREZ PUZZLERS

1. What U.S. president had the most children?

2. Who was the first Roman Catholic president?
(Hint: He was also the youngest president ever voted to office.)

3. Five presidents have last names that begin with a vowel. How many can you name?

4. Which chief executive had the shortest presidency?

5. What president was a five-star general?

ANSWERS: 1.John Tyler,15 2.John F. Kennedy 3.John Adams, John Quincy Adams, Chester A. Arthur, Dwight D. Eisenhower, and Barack Obama 4.William Henry Harrison... He died after only a month in office in 1841. 5.Dwight D. Eisenhower

Why do they call it the restroom?
Is there anybody just resting in this room?
-Dane Cook

Don't trust your wife's judgment. Look at what she married.

The top selling cereal in the United States is Cheerios. Second is Frosted Flakes.

•

The original price of a Barbie doll in 1959 was $3.

•

Maine lays claim to being the toothpick capital of the world.

•

Rattlesnakes are terrified of skunks.

•

The average weight of a dead person's ashes is nine pounds.

•

A Koala bear sleeps about 22 hours a day.

27,000 trees are chopped down each day for toilet paper.

Charles Ponzi, the man who created the illegal Ponzi scheme and made as much as $250,000 a day, died a pauper.

•

"World Wide Web" is three syllables when spoken. Its abbreviation, "www", is nine syllables.

•

There are about nine chickens for every human being in the world.

•

Nolan Bushnell founded Atari and Chuck E. Cheese.

•

New Jersey is the most densely populated state in the U.S. Maybe that's why it's also the state with the highest car insurance rates.

•

The mango is the most popular fruit on Earth, consumed worldwide by a factor of three to one over bananas and ten to one over apples.

> *I like to buy a four-pack of toilet paper every time I shop, just so I can ask the store clerk this judgment question: 'Would you say I got the right amount of toilet paper for the groceries I just bought?'*
> *-Pat Hazell*

DOCTORING IT UP

The answer to each of these clues is a doctor of sorts.

1. It was the pseudonym of author Theodore Geisel.

2. Harrison Ford played him in "The Fugitive."

3. Chemist R.S. Lazenby of Waco, Texas invented this in the Old Corner Drug Store in 1885.

4. Hugh Laurie played this free-wheeling, brilliant diagnostician on the FOX TV series.

5. This best-selling baby book author won a gold medal in rowing at the 1924 Olympics.

ANSWERS: 1.Dr. Seuss 2.Dr. Richard Kimble 3.Dr Pepper (Make no mistake about it – There's no period after the "Dr".) 4.Dr. Gregory House, of "House" 5.Dr. Benjamin Spock

RED, WHITE AND BLUE

1. He's the editor of the "Daily Planet" in the Superman flicks.

2. What big league baseball team changed its name for a while during the Cold War with Russia?

3. What was once painted grey and called the Executive Mansion?

4. By what other name has Broadway been known?

5. This is one of baseball's greatest trivia questions: Who was the last switch-hitter to win the AL MVP Award?

ANSWERS: 1.Perry White 2.The Cincinnati Reds (as in Soviets) changed their name to the Red Legs. 3.The White House 4.The Great White Way 5.Vida Blue, a pitcher, in 1971

You know you're getting fat when you sit in your bathtub and the water in the toilet rises.
-Etta May

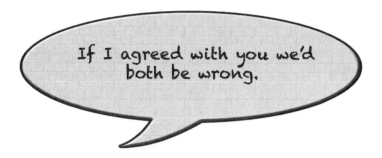

If I agreed with you we'd both be wrong.

Snickers, the most popular candy bar in the U.S., was introduced in 1930 and named for a horse owned by the candy's makers, the Mars family.

•

Ants do not sleep.

•

The only word in the English language with four pairs of double letters in a row is "subbookkeeper."

•

Sphenopalatine ganglioneuralgia is better known as "brain freeze" (that headache you get when you've swallowed too much ice cream).

•

Horses can't vomit.

The average clean-shaven man will spend five months of his life shaving.

Florida and North Dakota share the unshakeable honor of being the two states which have the fewest earthquakes.

•

The humuhumunukunukuapua'a is the state fish of Hawaii. It translates roughly to "the fish with a pig-like nose."

•

Take the bus! People are 80 times more likely to be killed while walking to school than while taking the bus.

•

President Thomas Jefferson despised formal affairs and would often greet foreign dignitaries while wearing pajamas.

•

The ostrich is the fastest two-legged creature on Earth, reaching a speed of 45 mph over short distances.

•

Zenith created the first TV remote control in 1950. It was called "Lazy Bones."

If you don't want your dog to have bad breath, do what I do: Pour a little Lavoris in the toilet.

-Jay Leno

Knowledge is knowing a tomato is a fruit; Wisdom is not putting it in a fruit salad.

Underneath It All

Try this "fact or flush?" quiz on for size.

1. The word "wedgie" comes from "wedge-heeled shoe" and became popular in the 1970s from the effect it gave the victim.

2. Roy Raymond invented the thong in 1977.

3. Women in Italy celebrate the New Year by wearing red underwear because it is considered lucky.

4. In 1951, Marlon Brando helped turn men's cotton undershirts into outerwear when he wore an undershirt in the movie "A Streetcar Named Desire."

5. "Long Johns" were originally worn by bare-knuckled boxer John L. Sullivan in the late 1800s.

6. In 2012, Zimbabwe banned the importation and sale of second-hand underwear.

7. The average American woman owns approximately 30 pairs of underwear.

8. In 1913, Mary Phelps Jacob took two silk handkerchiefs and tied them together with a pink ribbon, thus creating the first brassiere.

9. BVD, as in underwear, stands for the manufacturers names, Bradley, Voorhees and Day.

10. Umar Farouk Abdulmutallab introduced underwear to Nigeria in 1976, where natives went commando before his import of the product.

ANSWERS: 1.Fact 2.Flush- Raymond started the Victoria's Secret chain that year in San Francisco. 3.Fact 4.Fact 5.Fact- he wore long woolen drawers while boxing in cold weather. 6.Fact- Authorities hope the ban will aid health concerns and help the country's own domestic textile industry. 7.Flush- the average woman has 21 pairs of underwear- and 10% own over 35 pairs. 8.Fact 9.Fact 10.Flush- Abdulmutallab is known as the "Underwear Bomber," who unsuccessfully attempted to detonate explosives in his underpants on a Detroit-bound airplane on Christmas Day in 2009.

In the Middle Ages, they had guillotines, stretch racks, whips, and chains. Nowadays, we have a much more effective torture device called the bathroom scale.
-Stephen Phillips

Charles Douglass invented canned laughter.

•

"ETAOINSHRDLU" is a combination of the 12 most-commonly used letters in English, in descending order.

•

The phrase "going commando" stems from the Vietnam War, a time when American soldiers spent long periods of time in hot, humid jungles. Troops would go commando rather than wear tight-fitting undies which reduced ventilation and increased the risk of fungal infections in the groin area.

•

Augie, a golden retriever from Dallas, Texas, owns the doggie world record for holding tennis balls in the mouth, with 5.

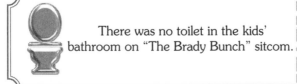

There was no toilet in the kids' bathroom on "The Brady Bunch" sitcom.

According to a "National Geographic" report, if the whole world was populated as densely as New York City, we would all fit into the state of Texas.

•

The 1974 Bethel High School, Brandt, Ohio, football team just might be the worst ever. They were shut out in all 10 games: 40-0, 53-0, 92-0, 89-0, 50-0, 56-0, 36-0, 33-0, 46-0, and 49-0. The coach's name: Dennis Reck.

•

Yahoo! is an acronym which stands for "Yet Another Hierarchical Officious Oracle."

•

Kleenex tissues were originally marketed as a cold cream remover.

•

Brett Favre's first pass completion as a Green Bay Packer was to himself.

•

Marie Osmond's first name is Olive.

*I have a very silly sense of humor.
I've never laughed harder in my entire life
than seeing someone with toilet paper stuck
on the bottom of their shoe.*
-Paula Poundstone

The best things in life are free-- plus shipping and handling.

MINDING YOUR P'S AND Q'S

The solutions to these clues all begin with "p" or "q".

1. A statue honoring this naval cartoon hero stands in Crystal City, Texas.

2. This sport bans lefties.

3. It's the airline to Australia.

4. Remove the last four letters of this five-letter word and it's still pronounced the same.

5. A.C. Gilbert, the inventor of the erector set, scaled new heights when he won an Olympic gold medal in 1908 in this event.

ANSWERS: 1.Popeye 2.Polo 3.Qantas 4.Queue 5.Pole vault

The official color of San Francisco's Golden Gate Bridge is "International Orange."

•

Amerigo Vespucci, the man many believe for whom America was named, was an Italian pickle merchant.

•

Teddy Roosevelt's first wife and mother died in the same house, on the same day- Valentine's Day of 1884.

•

Dogs can get laryngitis from too much barking.

•

Until the 1970s in rural America, some funeral homes made their hearses available for use as ambulances to transport patients to hospitals.

•

Your feet make up 1/4 of the bones in your entire body.

•

Cotton candy is called fairy floss in Australia.

Endangered forests are being slaughtered for toilet paper.
-Daphne Zuniga

Hummingbirds don't know the words.

TIME AND TIME AGAIN

1. What is the third hand on a clock called?

2. An extremely odd happenstance occurred in 1978 on the 6th of May at 12:34 p.m. Do you know what it was?

3. True or false? Any month that starts on a Sunday will have a Friday the 13th.

4. If a centennial relates to a period of 100 years, to what does a decennial relate?

5. What kind of year has 31,622,400 seconds in it?

ANSWERS: 1.The second hand 2.At that exact moment, the time read 12:34, 5/6/78. 3.True 4.A period of 10 years 5.Leap year

Elvis Presley died while reading in the bathroom.

The hippopotamus is thought to be the most dangerous animal in Africa, killing more humans annually than lions, crocodiles, or snakes.

•

First Lady Julia Tyler used the title "Mrs. Presidentress" when her husband, John, was the POTUS.

•

William Wrigley was in the baking powder business and gave a free pack of his gum with each box of his product. When he discovered that people were buying it just to get the gum, he didn't have to chew on it very long to realize he should switch businesses.

•

Neil Armstrong's astronaut application arrived a week past the deadline, but a friend slipped his form into the pile before anyone could notice.

•

The plane can only be called "Air Force One" when the President of the United States is on it.

You never really realize what you have 'til it's gone... A good example of that is toilet paper.
-Chuckie Ward

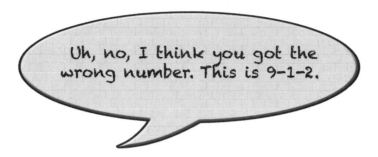

Ben Franklin's formal education stopped at the age of 10.

•

The average couch potato will burn about 60 to 70 calories an hour just by sitting in front of the TV. That, of course, does not include indulging in snacks at the same time.

•

On March 15th, 1985, symbolics.com became the first registered domain name.

•

That orange-handled pot which signifies decaffeinated coffee was introduced back in 1923, when General Foods was promoting Sanka and provided restaurants with pots to match the orange packaging of their new brew.

•

Not only does a tiger have striped fur. It has striped skin, too!

Better Known As...

• Stefani Joanne Angelina Germanotta's stage name is Lady Gaga.

• Jonathan Stuart Leibowitz is better known as Jon Stewart.

• Aubrey Graham is known as Drake.

• Paul David Hewson is known as Bono.

• You know Louis Szekely as a comedian by the name of Louis C.K.

• Oscar-winning actor Sir Ben Kingsley was born Krishna Pandit Bhanji.

• Dwayne Michael Carter, Jr., became Lil Wayne.

• Thomas DeCarlo Callaway is better known as Cee Lo Green.

NASA asked me to create meals for the space shuttle. Thai chicken was the favorite. I flew in a fake space shuttle, but I have no desire to go into space after seeing the toilet.
-Rachel Ray

A dog has an owner.
A cat has a staff.

HORSEPLAY

1. He was horse racing's last Triple Crown winner.

2. What's the longest amount of letters a racing horse can have in its name?

3. What is a farrier?

4. What "first" occurred when it left St. Joseph, Missouri, on April 3, 1860?

5. What's the drink du jour of the Kentucky Derby?

ANSWERS: 1.Affirmed, in 1978 2.18 3.A horse shoer... There are some 15,000 farriers in the U.S. 4.The first Pony Express 5.Mint julep

Smartphones have more germs than a subway station toilet, so says a 2010 Journal of Applied Microbiology study. Sharing the phones is just as apt to spread bacteria as sneezing in someone's face.

MOTHERS OF INVENTION

1. What invention was originally called the "Epsicle?"

2. What inventor holds the most patents?

3. What is it that Daisuke Inoue invented in 1971?
(Hint: Think "Sing Along With Mitch.")

4. Ermal Cleon Fraze went on a family picnic in 1959, but forgot to bring a can opener, forcing him to use his car bumper to open the can. It later inspired him to invent what useful device?

5. Who invented charcoal briquettes?

ANSWERS: 1.The popsicle....Invented by11-year-old Frank Epperson when he accidentally left a glass of punch with a stick in it on his porch overnight. He renamed it when applying for the patent, reportedly because his kids referred to the ice delight as "Pop's sicle." 2.Thomas Edison, of course... The Wizard of Menlo Park holds 1,093 patents.3.The karaoke machine 4.The pop-top can opener 5.Automobile pioneer Henry Ford

I walk into rooms and I don't know why I'm there. I'm like, 'Why am I standing in front of the toilet now?'
-Matthew Broderick

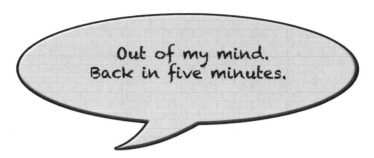

Before Beverly Hills became fertile ground for the rich and famous, it was known for its lima beans.

•

The NFL's Kansas City Chiefs were named after the mayor of Kansas City, H. Roe Bartle, nicknamed "The Chief". Bartle was chiefly responsible for bringing the Dallas Texans to Kansas City in 1963 so owner Lamar Hunt renamed the team in honor of him.

•

How many Wright Brothers were there? Four, actually. Wilbur and Orville had two older brothers, Reuchlin and Lorin. They had a younger sister, too- Katharine.

•

Henry Wadsworth Longfellow's wife died tragically by fire after a dropped match ignited her dress.

•

Elvis Presley's hair was a natural dirty blond. He began dying his hair in 1957 to copy Tony Curtis, Elvis' favorite actor.

The Vatican Bank boasts the only ATM machines in the world where users can perform transactions in Latin.

•

O'Hare Airport is named after Lieutenant Commander Butch O'Hare, who was the son of Al Capone's lawyer.

•

The first person to survive going over Niagara Falls in a barrel was a 63-year-old schoolteacher named Annie Edson Taylor.

•

The very first item sold on eBay was a broken laser pointer bought by a collector. He paid $14.83.

•

The highest temperature ever recorded on earth was 136° F in Al Aziziyah, Libya back on September 13, 1922.

•

Only the female mosquito will bite you.

Life is like a movie-since there aren't any commercial breaks, you have to get up and go to the bathroom in the middle of it.
-Garry Trudeau

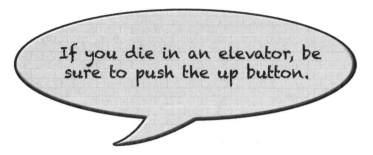

If you die in an elevator, be sure to push the up button.

Whatchamacallits

• The slash between fractions (2/3) and words (and/or) is a "virgule."

• The ball on the top of a flagpole is known as the "truck."

• No doubt you're familiar with that paper ribbon on the top of a Hershey's Kiss. It has a name- it's a "niggly wiggly."

• The snapping sound made between your thumb and middle finger is a "fillip."

• If your second toe is bigger than your big toe, you have what's called "Morton's toe."

The average person uses about fifty-seven sheets of toilet paper each day.

• The infinity symbol is called a "lemniscate."

• The side opposite the hammer's striking side is the "peen."

• The little bumps on a ping-pong paddle are called "pips." So are the dots on dice.

• That ridge between your upper lip and nose is the "philtrum."

• The protective point or knob on the end of an umbrella is a "ferrule."

• The cardboard sleeve that's wrapped around your hot coffee is called a "zarf."

• Those long strings that you get while peeling a banana are known as "phloem bundles."

• The combination of a question and an exclamation mark (?!) is called an "interrobang."

You do live longer with bran, but you spend the last fifteen years on the toilet.
-Alan King

The Rose Bowl was originally called the Battle of the Flowers.

•

Those that know Mr. Clean on a first name basis call him "Veritably." The name was chosen in a promotion in the early 1960s.

•

A group of rhinos is known as a "crash."

•

If Dr. Phil, George Foreman or Bruce Willis give you the willies, maybe you're suffering from peladophobia- a fear of bald people.

•

Coulrophobia is a fear of clowns.

•

During an advertising campaign in 1907, Kellogg's Corn Flakes offered a free box of cereal to any woman who would wink at her grocer.

JACK OF ALL TRADES

1. He hosted the "Tonight Show" before Johnny Carson.

2. Can you name the action film star who was born Chan Kong-sang?

3. Born Benjamin Kubelsky, this comedian grew up in Waukegan, Illinois, and was forever 39 years old.

4. His number "42" was retired permanently by Major League Baseball.

5. You'll find twelve of them on the four of them in a deck of them. Identify "them".

ANSWERS: 1.Jack Paar 2.Jackie Chan 3.Jack Benny 4.Jackie Robinson 5.There are twelve eyes on the four jacks in a deck of cards (two one-eyed jacks shown right side up and upside down and a pair of two-eyed jacks, also shown right side up and upside down).

It is better to have a relationship with someone who cheats on you than with someone who does not flush the toilet.
-Uma Thurman

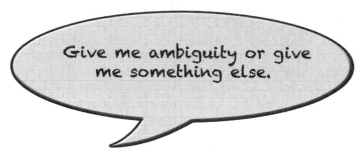

Give me ambiguity or give me something else.

The duffel bag was so named because the cloth originally used in the bags came from Duffel, Belgium.

•

An octopus has three hearts.

•

If you take your age and multiply it by 7, then multiply it by 1,443 the answer repeats your age 3 times.

•

The opening line to Jerome K. Jerome's "Three Men In A Boat" is: 'There were four of us.'

•

Charles Blondin crossed Niagara Falls many times in many ways on a 1,000-foot tightrope: blindfolded, on stilts, in a sack, carrying a man on his back and cooking an omelette in the middle.

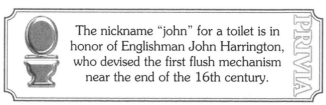

The nickname "john" for a toilet is in honor of Englishman John Harrington, who devised the first flush mechanism near the end of the 16th century.

Japan has square watermelons.

•

Picasso was one of the suspects when the Mona Lisa was stolen from the Louvre in 1911.

•

An 'earworm' is a song that sticks in your mind even when it's not playing.

•

Sir Edmund Hillary, the first man to climb Mt. Everest, was a professional beekeeper.

•

In 1897, Felix Hoffman invented both aspirin and heroin.

•

Michael J. Fox's middle name is Andrew.

•

The highest scoring word in Scrabble is... oxyphenbutazone, with a potential total of 1,178 points. (It's a drug used to treat arthritis.)

Now what I don't get are those people who, instead of buying a four-pack or an eight-pack of toilet paper, they buy the single individual roll. Are you trying to quit?

-Brian Kiley

CANDYLAND

1. Who is the Baby Ruth candy bar named after?
(It wasn't the baseball player!)

2. How about M&M's?

3. What chocolate, chewy candy did Austrian Leo Hirshfield bring to the U.S. in 1896?

4. "Taste the Rainbow" is the slogan of what candy?

5. Life Savers were invented by Clarence Crane, ironically, in the same year the Titanic sunk. What year?

ANSWERS 1.Ruth Cleveland, the daughter of President Grover Cleveland. 2.M&M's, first sold in 1941, were named for their developers, Forrest Mars and Bruce Murries. 3.The Tootsie Roll 4.Skittles 5.1912

Fidel Castro calculated that he saved ten working days a year by not bothering to shave.

•

The word ambisinistrous is an antonym of ambidextrous; it means 'no good with either hand.'

•

Bobby Leach was the second man to go over Niagara Falls in a barrel. He survived that fall but later died as a result of slipping on a piece of orange peel.

•

"Feedback" and "boldface" are the shortest words in the English language which contain A,B,C,D,E, and F.

•

The smallest number that can be exactly divided by all the numbers 1 to 10 is 2,520.

•

When Einstein published his Theory of General Relativity, the "New York Times" covered it to a tee. They sent their golfing correspondent to interview him.

I found out why cats drink out of the toilet. My mother told me it's because the water is cold in there. And I'm like, how did my mother know that?

-Wendy Liebman

HARDBALL TRIVIA

1. How many feet is it from home plate to second base on a major league diamond?

2. What's the score of a forfeited big league game?

3. Can a pitcher's glove be green?

4. Where is the Little League World Series played?

5. How about the College World Series?

ANSWERS: 1.127 feet, 3 3/8 inches 2.9-0 3.Yes... It may be any solid color except white or gray. 4.Williamsport, Pennsylvania 5.Omaha, Nebraska

National Bathroom Reading Week
is celebrated annually during the
first full week of June.

The population of Facebook is more than one billion. If it was a country, it would be the third largest on the planet.

•

Only 35% of the average person's Twitter followers are actually people.

•

The United States has only 5% of the world's people, but close to 25% of its prison population.

•

Feeding canaries red peppers can make them turn orange.

•

Every U.S. president with a beard has been Republican.

•

The most shoplifted book in the USA is The Bible.

•

Only two animals have chins- humans and elephants.

European toilet paper is made from the same material that Americans use for roofing, which is why Europeans tend to remain standing throughout soccer matches.

-Dave Barry

Humpty Dumpty was pushed.

Beavers have transparent eyelids so they can see underwater with their eyes shut.

•

In 2008, Usain Bolt set the 100 meters world record with one shoelace undone.

•

It's never happened, but if their mating was successful, the offspring of a male jaguar and female tiger would be known as a 'jagger.'

•

Names which were on the drawing board for Walt Disney's seven dwarfs included Burpy, Baldy, Biggo-Ego, Dirty, Shifty, Flabby and Lazy.

•

The plural of the Toyota Prius is Prii.

•

There are more than 35,000 golf courses in the world, with about half of them in the U.S.

Construction on the Pentagon began on September 11, 1941, 60 years to the day before the terrorist attacks of September 11, 2001.

•

One of Ronald Reagan's pet names for Nancy Reagan was 'Mommy Poo Pants.'

•

A squirrel can remember the hiding places of up to 10,000 nuts.

•

Most bees buzz in the key of A, but when tired, they buzz in the key of E.

•

Two-thirds of the people in the world have never seen snow.

•

The first commercial chewing gum appeared in 1871 after Thomas Adams unsuccessfully tried to make car tires from the same ingredients.

> *I don't know if I want a fuzzy cover on my toilet seat, but I want to meet whoever invented them. Who lifted a toilet seat and thought, 'That needs a hat'?*
>
> *-Rita Rudner*

"The difficult thing with quotes on the Internet is verifying them."
—Benjamin Franklin

PRESIDENTIAL POOCHES

1. The Obamas' Portuguese Water Dog is named...?

2. True or false? President James Garfield owned a dog named Veto.

3. Gerald Ford's dog, Liberty, gave birth to nine puppies in the White House. What breed was Liberty?

4. Buddy was his pal.

5. Beagle, Little Beagle, Him and Her sniffed around the White House during whose tenure in the '60s?

ANSWERS: 1."Bo" 2.True 3.Golden retriever 4.Bill Clinton's 5.Lyndon Johnson's

 Approximately three-quarters of fresh water usage in American homes occurs in the bathroom.

Formerly known as...

Google was originally called BackRub.

Elmer Fudd was originally known as Egghead.

Red Bull was known as Red Water Buffalo.

Austin, Texas, was first named Waterloo.

Kool-Aid was once marketed as Fruit Smack.

eBay was AuctionWeb.

The Baby Ruth bar was originally called Kandy Kake.

7-Up was first marketed as Bib-Label Lithiated Lemon-Lime Soda.

Red-Hot Chili Peppers was first named Tony Flow and the Miraculously Majestic Masters of Mayhem.

When someone follows you all the way to the shop and watches you buy a toilet roll, you know your life has changed.
-Jennifer Aniston

All polar bears are Irish. They are descendants of brown bears that lived in Ireland over 10,000 years ago.

•

Astronauts cannot whistle while they work. A whistle can't be heard in space.

•

11 of the 12 astronauts who walked on the Moon were Boy Scouts.

•

Despite a decade of playing the Fonz on "Happy Days," Henry Winkler never learned to ride a motorcycle.

•

In Italy, 17 is an unlucky number, not 13.

•

President Obama's secret-service nickname is 'Renegade.' Ronald Reagan's nickname was 'Rawhide', Bill Clinton's was 'Eagle' and George W. Bush's monicker was 'Trailblazer.'

Most domestic cats can run faster than Usain Bolt.

•

The praying mantis has only one ear and it's located between its legs.

•

Only 5% of white American adults are naturally blond.

•

There are more plastic lawn flamingos in the U.S. than real ones.

•

If you ever wondered how tall grass can get, if it's bamboo- which is grass –it can grow up to 120 feet.

•

"1661" is slang for an older woman who dresses in young fashions, or a woman who looks "16 from the back, but 61 in front."

•

Orangutans belch as a warning signal to stay away from their territory.

Maybe they should have a toilet paper museum... So we can all see the toilet paper advancements down through the ages. Toilet paper in the Crusades: The development of the perforation. The first six-pack.

-Jerry Seinfeld

Deja moo: The feeling that you've heard this bull before.

D-DAY

1. What does the D in HDTV stand for?

2. Name the baseball Hall of Fame pitching great known as "Big D."

3. D is what number in Roman numerals?

4. What is the Greek equivalent to the letter D?

5. French explorer Antoine Laumet de La Mothe, sieur de Cadillac founded this city in 1701. Was it "D" as in Dallas, Detroit, or Des Moines?

ANSWERS: 1.Definition, as in High Definition TV 2.Don Drysdale 3.500 4.Delta 5.Detroit

Joseph Gayetty invented toilet paper in 1857 and we have British inventor Walter Alcock to thank for his 1879 ideas to perforate the paper and put it on a roll.

TRIVIA

TESTING, TESTING

1. Louise Brown became known as the first baby of this kind on July 25, 1978.

2. Its name means "table" in Latin and it is the largest high-IQ society in the world, open to those who have achieved in the upper two percent of the general population on standardized tests.

3. What would you be tested for if you were looking at the Snellen Chart?

4. What psychological exam is commonly known as the Ink Blot Test?

5. DNA testing is commonplace these days, but not so commonly known is what DNA stands for. Do you?

ANSWERS: 1.Test tube baby 2.Mensa 3.Your eyesight- It's that chart with the big E on top. 4.The Rorschach Test 5.Deoxyribonucleic acid

I grew up with six brothers.
That's how I learned to dance-
waiting for the bathroom.
-Bob Hope

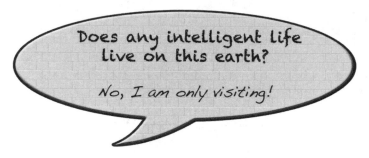

According to "Business Insider," Apple is the most valuable brand name in the world, followed by Google and IBM.

•

Dead skin cells make up about 90% of all household dust.

•

The tortoise can live to be 140 years old.

•

Giraffes sleep an average of 1.9 hours a day.

•

Because of its proximity to Lake Erie, Cleveland was sometimes derided as the "Mistake on the Lake." Fact of the matter is that Cleveland itself is a typo. The city's founder was Moses Cleaveland and no one knows why the letter A disappeared in the 1830s.

•

Oscar the Grouch was orange for the first season of "Sesame Street."

TWOFERS

1. Bruce Wayne and Dick Grayson were the secret identities of what superheroes?

2. Cohen and Greenfield own a national ice cream chain that bears the duo's first names. What are they?

3. Leonard Slye and Frances Octavia Smith were the real names of what famous TV western married couple of the 1950s?

4. This comic duo is beloved by children the world over and in Spain they're referred to as "Epi y Blas". What do we call them here in the U.S.A.?

5. True or false? Marc Anthony was married to Cleopatra.

ANSWERS: 1.Batman and Robin 2.Ben and Jerry 3.Roy Rogers and Dale Evans 4.Bert and Ernie 5.False- Mark Antony was married to Cleopatra. Marc Anthony was married to Jennifer Lopez.

I'm always so confused when I see a toilet seat up in the ladies restroom.
-Unknown

When everything's coming your way, you're in the wrong lane.

In its first years, the 3 Musketeers candy bar came in three pieces and three flavors- vanilla, chocolate and strawberry, hence the name.

•

Fredric Bauer was the inventor of the Pringles can. When he died in 2008, his ashes were buried in one.

•

The only state in the U.S. that can be typed on one row of keys is Alaska.

•

If you have a condition known as rhinotillexomania, you are an obsessive nose picker.

•

The average midfield soccer player runs close to seven miles per game.

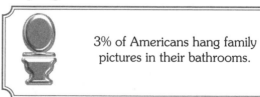

3% of Americans hang family pictures in their bathrooms.

In the 1950s, Rice Krispies featured Snap, Crackle, Pop and a fourth gnome- Pow, who represented the cereal's explosive nutritional power.

•

Hawaiian Punch made its debut in 1934 as a tropical flavored ice cream topping.

•

You'd have to go way back to 1928 to find a time a Republican was elected president without a Nixon or Bush on the ticket.

•

The space between your thumb and extended forefinger is called the purlicue.

•

Cows are inclined to give more milk when they listen to music.

•

Abraham Lincoln's mother died after drinking poisonous milk from the family's dairy cow.

I sometimes feel alone and insignificant, especially when people turn out the lights while I'm still in the bathroom.
-Steven Wright

Take my advice;
I don't use it anyway.

The Fear of It

"The only thing we have to fear is fear itself."

Franklin Delano Roosevelt's words are an apt description of "phobophobia"- a fear of fears. Trusting that you're not suffering from that particular condition, here are some obscure phobias of the famous.

• Oprah Winfrey suffers from the rare phobia known as chiclephobia, or the fear of chewing gum.

• Pamela Anderson has eisoptrophobia, a fear of mirrors.

• Nicole Kidman has lepidopterophobia. She is terrified of butterflies.

• George Washington had taphephobia, a fear of being buried alive.

• Richard Nixon suffered from nosocomephobia, a fear of hospitals.

• Alfred Hitchcock had ovophobia, a fear of eggs.

• Napoleon Bonaparte had ailurophobia. He was afraid of cats.

• Barbra Streisand is xenophobic, uncomfortable around strangers.

• Britney Spears has herpetophobia, a fear of reptiles.

• David Beckham claims to have ataxophobia, a fear of disorder or untidiness.

• Christina Ricci suffers from botanaphobia, which is a fear of house plants.

• Justin Timberlake is arachnophobic – he has a fear of spiders.

• Keanu Reeves is a scotophobic who dreads darkness.

• Madonna suffers from brontophobia, the fear of thunder.

Show me a nation whose national beverage is beer, and I'll show you an advanced toilet technology.
-Paul Hawkins

All my imaginary friends think I am crazy.

DOWN AND DIRTY

1. Clint Eastwood starred as Harry Callaghan in the title role of this 1971 crime thriller.

2. He was the co-host of NBC's "Today" and anchor of ABC's "20/20."

3. Patrick Swayze and Jennifer Grey starred in this 1987 romantic flick.

4. It's the address of the Prime Minister of Great Britain.

5. A hit pop recording by Men at Work, it's quite naturally a popular patriotic song in Australia.

ANSWERS: 1."Dirty Harry" 2.Hugh Downs 3."Dirty Dancing" 4.10 Downing Street 5."Down Under"

Brad Pitt and Angelina Jolie have a custom-made bathtub carved from a single piece of limestone, the same stone which makes up the 3-inch thick walls of the entire bathroom.

Light bulb inventor Thomas Edison was afraid of the dark.

•

Someone who suffers from "prosopagnosia" is unable to recognize faces, including their own image in a mirror.

•

Hyundai, as in the car, means "modernity" in Korean.

•

In 2005, when Jawed Karim became frustrated at not being able to easily locate a video clip of Janet Jackson's Super Bowl halftime wardrobe malfunction, he and his two buddies at PayPal- Steve Chen and Chad Hurley – created just the remedy for that sort of thing: YouTube.

•

A ticket to the Beatles' concert at Shea Stadium in New York in 1965 cost $5.65.

•

Warning: Don't try this at home. On average, a Twinkie will explode in 45 seconds when put in the microwave.

My family tree was chopped down and they made the lumber into toilet paper. We've never been closer.
-Barry Steiger

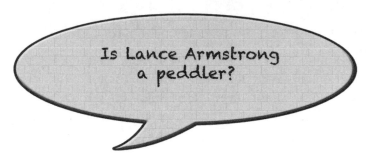

Is Lance Armstrong a peddler?

Oscar winner Tommy Lee Jones and former vice-president Al Gore were college roommates at Harvard.

•

Monkeys don't have feet and are classified as four-handed.

•

Dr. Seuss wrote "Green Eggs and Ham" after he was challenged by his editor to come up with a book using fewer than fifty different words.

•

Eat a typical one-ounce serving of Cheerios and you'll eat 400 "O's."

•

The only word in the English language with five consecutive vowels is "queueing."

•

A jellyfish is 95% water.

START TO FINISH

1. Four states begin and end with the same letter. How many can you name?

2. This famous pop music group fashioned their four-letter name, beginning and ending with the same letter, after a Swedish fish-canning company.

3. This city, which begins ands with the letter "S", is home to the Jefferson National Expansion Memorial.

4. This actor, who has the same first and last initials, got off to a rocky show biz start in 1976 with his Oscar-winning picture.

5. It's a ten-letter word that has a "k" at the beginning and end, and a hyphen in the middle.

ANSWERS: 1.Alabama, Alaska, Arizona and Ohio 2.Abba
3.The Jefferson National Expansion Memorial, also called the
Gateway Arch, is in St. Louis, MO. 4.Sylvester Stallone 5.Knick-knack

The baby is great. My wife and I have just started potty training. Which I think is important, because when we want to potty train the baby we should set an example.

-Howie Mandel

I was an iWitness at an
Apple Store robbery.

Bubble gum is pink simply because Walter Diemer, who
worked at Fleer, had only pink coloring left when he
mixed up his first successful concoction.

•

7-Eleven was first known as Tote'm Stores when it
opened in Dallas in 1927.

•

The thong, as in swimsuit, is known as fio dental or
"dental floss" in Brazil.

•

An octopus has nine brains- one for each of its arms and
one in the head.

•

You're more likely to die while traveling to buy a lottery
ticket than you are to actually win the lottery.

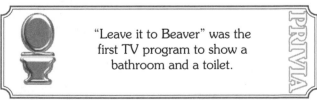

"Leave it to Beaver" was the
first TV program to show a
bathroom and a toilet.

PRIVIA

The One and Only

Utah is the only state in the U.S. with an official snack-Jell-O.

• •

The only word spoken in Mel Brooks' "Silent Movie" was "Non!,"uttered by the French mime Marcel Marceau.

• •

George Washington was the only president to never live in the White House.

• •

The only part of the body that can't repair itself is the tooth.

• •

Sister Mary Carolyn was the only nun to be mayor of a city. She was elected Mayor of Dubuque, Iowa, in 1980.

• •

The Dalmatian is the only dog that can get gout.

Why do men have to put the toilet seat down after using the toilet, if women don't have to put it back up when they're done?

-Anonymous

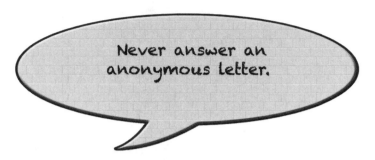

Never answer an anonymous letter.

In springtime, a wild male turkey's head can turn a brilliant red, white or blue in a matter of moments.

•

Yawning is contagious. As a matter of fact, there's a 50% chance you're about to feel a yawn coming on right now.

•

Anatidaephobia is the fear that somewhere on the planet there is a duck watching you.

•

A person will swallow an average of about 250 times during dinner.

•

Cars are more likely to be stolen on New Year's Day than any other day of the year.

•

Marilu Henner, of "Taxi" sitcom fame, is one of only 20 people in the world who's been identified with "hyperthymesia," the ability to recall events from every day of her life.

The first x-rated movie to win the Best Picture Oscar was "Midnight Cowboy."

•

George Washington needed to borrow money to go to his own inauguration.

•

The sound you hear when you crack your knuckles is gas bubbles bursting.

•

Dolphins can't smell.

•

The most common street name in the U.S. is Second Street.

•

A group of owls is called a parliament.

•

Nine out of ten American children visit a McDonald's every month.

> *If you're embarking around the world in a hot-air balloon, don't forget the toilet paper.*
> *-Richard Branson*

Why isn't "phonetics" spelled the way it sounds?

Pinocchio is Italian for "pine head."

•

Grapes will explode if you try to microwave them.

•

A cow's life span is 30 years.

•

The only fifteen-letter word that is spelled without repeating a letter is "uncopyrightable."

•

The first hearing aid was as big as a suitcase.

•

The only word in the English language that ends in 'mt' is dreamt.

In 1840, poet Henry Wadsworth Longfellow became the first American to have plumbing installed in his house.

PRIVIA

Setting the Record Straight

• Black-eyed peas are not peas. They are beans.

• The Douglas fir is not a fir. It is a pine tree.

• No one "eats like a bird." Birds eat up to half their body weight every day!

• Centipedes do not have one hundred feet- most of them, anyway. The centipede has anywhere from 28 to 354 legs.

• Money is not the root of all evil according to the Bible. Biblical verse says, "For the love of money is the root of all evil."

• The Hundred Years War lasted 116 years.

• Ostriches do not bury their heads in the sand- they wouldn't be able to breathe!

• French poodles originated in Germany.

If I'm sitting on the toilet and I'm looking at the grouting on the tiles, that grouting really gets me. Mothers have a thing about grouting.
-Sharon Osbourne

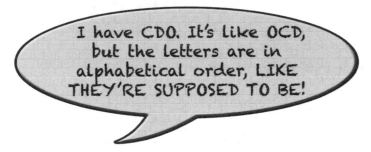

• Chinese checkers did not come from China. It originated in England.

• A pony is not a baby horse. It is a small horse of any age (generally less than 58 inches tall).

• The standard lumber known as a two-by-four is not two-by-four. It is typically 1 5/8" x 3 5/8".

• A ten-gallon hat does not hold ten gallons. It holds about three quarts.

• Panama hats do not come from Panama. They come from Ecuador.

• Fortune cookies do not come from China. They were invented in 1918 in the United States.

• The funny bone is not a bone. It is a nerve.

• The westernmost part of the United States is not in Hawaii. It's in Alaska.

THE SPORTS PAGE

1. What NFL team has won the most Super Bowls: Steelers or Cowboys?

2. On a baseball scorecard, what does a "K" signify?

3. Fact or fib? The Olympic flame was conceived for the Games by none other than Adolf Hitler.

4. How long is a half in NCAA basketball?

5. In 1940, Cleveland ace Bob Feller hurled a 1-0 no-hitter against Chicago, yet none of the White Sox players' batting averages went up or down. How was this possible?

ANSWERS: 1.Steelers, 6 2.A swinging strikeout 3.Fact 4.20 minutes 5.It was Opening Day- the first and only no-hitter thrown at the beginning of a season.

Why does toilet paper need a commercial? Who is not buying this?
-Anonymous

Mona Lisa was framed.

A parrot's vocabulary is generally no more than twenty words.

•

In-between his many accomplishments, Benjamin Franklin gave guitar lessons.

•

You know that point on your back between your shoulder blades where you cannot reach to scratch? That's the "acnestis."

•

Fish can become seasick if kept on board a ship.

•

The tallest man in the world was Robert Wadlow. He was 22 when he died in 1949 from an infection caused by leg braces he needed to keep him on his feet.

70% of Americans say they close the bathroom door even when no one else is home.

7-UP

1. Which has more outlets, 7-Eleven or McDonald's?

2. Which one of Disney's seven dwarfs wears glasses?

3. Can you name the seven colors of the rainbow?

4. According to the old joke, if you ask how to get there you might be told, "Practice", but your GPS would lead you to Seventh Avenue and 57th Street. Where is this?

5. A simple yes or no- is the area code for Las Vegas 777?

ANSWERS: 1.7-Eleven- It is the world's biggest convenience store chain, with more than 39,000 retail locations. 2.Doc 3.Red, orange, yellow, green, blue, indigo and violet 4.Carnegie Hall 5.No- it is 702. There is no area code designated as 777.

> *I'm terribly lazy. That's why I like being in the movies. I'm performing all over the world – while I'm home taking a bath.*
> *-Barbra Streisand*

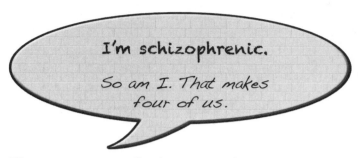

The average caterpillar has sixteen legs.

•

Martin Van Buren was the first U.S. born citizen to become president.

•

A flea expert is a pullicologist.

•

Lake Michigan is the only one of the Great Lakes which is entirely in the U.S.

•

Baboons cannot throw overhand.

•

Vincent van Gogh didn't begin to draw until he was 27.

•

Crows are thought to be the smartest birds.

•

Buckingham Palace is the former site of a brothel.

Ann Royall was the first woman journalist to interview a president. When John Quincy Adams was skinnydipping one day, she stole his clothes and would not give them back until he gave her an interview.

•

The word "karate" means empty hand.

•

The largest fruit crop on Earth is grapes.

•

If you take a penny and double it, and then keep doubling it every day for 30 days, you will wind up with over five million dollars.

•

Albert Einstein was four years old before he could even talk.

•

The reason you haven't seen any cashews in a shell is because they don't have any. The cashew is a seed, not a nut.

Why is it that Kmart won't take back underwear that's been opened, but they'll take back a toilet seat within 30 days?

-Nick Tarr

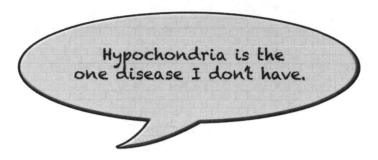

Hypochondria is the one disease I don't have.

When Dodger Stadium in Los Angeles opened in 1962, it had no drinking fountains.

•

A male kangaroo is called a boomer, a female is called a flyer and a baby kangaroo is a joey.

•

Right-handed people have a tendency to scratch with their left hand and vice-versa.

•

White is the most popular color for new cars.

•

A duck's quack does not echo.

According to a 1990s Scott Paper survey, two-thirds of the people who hold a master's degree or a doctorate read in the bathroom.

EXTRA! EXTRA!

1. This news website was established in 2005 and acquired by AOL in 2011.

2. The "daily diary of the American dream" is the slogan of what newspaper?

3. What's the most widely circulated Sunday newspaper in America?

4. "USA Today" is the widest circulated paper in the U.S., printing in all fifty states. How many days a week is it printed?

5. What paper is a primary news source for members of the U.S. military?

ANSWERS: 1."The Huffington Post" 2."Wall Street Journal" 3."New York Times" 4.Five- it does not print on weekends. 5."Stars and Stripes"

There's (sic) three things I hate:
the opera, the police station,
and cold toilet seats.

-Archie Bunker

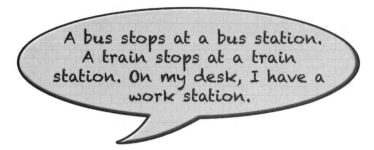

A bus stops at a bus station. A train stops at a train station. On my desk, I have a work station.

Footnotes

When all is said and done, if you're the average person, you'll walk around 15,000 miles when you're all said and done.

• •

Seven out of ten people will have painful foot problems in their lifetime.

• •

Confederate General Robert E. Lee wore a size 4 1/2.

• •

Barack and Michelle Obama both wear an 11 1/2 shoe. Of course, the first lady's is women's size.

• •

Ashton Kutcher has webbed toes.

• •

NFL Hall of Fame quarterback Troy Aikman was born with a clubfoot. He was in plaster casts as an infant and wore special shoes until he was three.

BEFORE OR AFTER?

1. Facebook was invented before or after the election of Barack Obama as President of the United States?

2. The first man on the moon set foot on the lunar surface before or after the first woman in space?

3. Did White Castle open before or after Burger King?

4. Did Martha Custis get married before or after George Washington?

5. In spelling, is "I before E, except after C" always true?

ANSWERS: 1.Before- Facebook made its debut in 2004. Obama was elected in '08. 2.After- The first man on the moon was Neil Armstrong in 1969, six years after Russian Valerie Tereshkova became the first woman in space. 3.Before- White Castle was the nation's first hamburger chain, opening in 1921. The first BK opened in 1954. 4.Before- Martha Custis was married to George Washington, but was also married before him- to Daniel Parke Custis. 5.No- there are many exceptions, like "science" and "sufficient", for example.

I stay there (the bathtub) for hours.
Sometimes I even fill it with water.
-Woody Allen

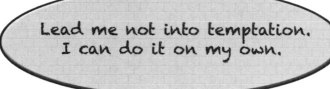

Lead me not into temptation. I can do it on my own.

Play-Doh was originally intended to be a wallpaper cleaner.

•

Iceberg lettuce derived its name from the 1920s, when it was shipped from California packed in ice.

•

Chef Boyardee was a real person. He was Hector Boiardi, an Italian immigrant who ran a Cleveland restaurant where he cooked up his special spaghetti sauce.

•

The real name of Korean hip hop artist Psy is Park Jae-sang.

•

The astronauts on Apollo 10 traveled faster than any humans ever, a speed of 25,000 miles per hour.

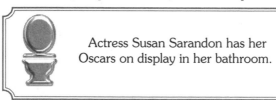

Actress Susan Sarandon has her Oscars on display in her bathroom.

PRIVIA

SAINTS ALIVE!

1. The New Orleans Saints football team was organized on November 1, which is the observance of what religious occasion?

2. What course in Scotland is regarded as the birthplace of golf?

3. The Pony Express route began in what Missouri city in 1860?

4. What river connects the Great Lakes with the Atlantic Ocean?

5. What is the oldest city the United States?

ANSWERS: 1.All Saints Day 2.St. Andrews 3.St. Joseph (finishing in Sacramento, California a year and a half later) 4.The St. Lawrence River 5.St. Augustine, Florida, founded in 1565

People who live in glass houses shouldn't use the bathroom.
-Anonymous

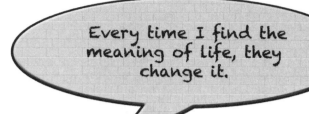

Every time I find the meaning of life, they change it.

Warning Signs

Somewhat silly suggestions printed on the
packaging of popular products...

• Dial Soap- *Directions: Use like regular soap*

• Sun-Maid raisins packet- *Why not try tossing over your
favorite breakfast cereal?*

• On a muffin wrapper at 7-Eleven- *Remove wrapper,
open mouth, insert muffin, eat.*

• Sears hair dryer- *Do not use while sleeping.*

• Heinz ketchup- *Instructions: Put on food*

• Swanson frozen dinner- *Serving suggestion: Defrost.*

• Silly Putty- *Do not use as ear plugs.*

• On a bag of Fritos- *You could be a winner!
No purchase necessary. Details inside.*

52 Miscellaneous Mindbenders

Sooo…you might be thinking, "52 questions…Why 52?" Well, we've got an ace up our sleeve - you! Pick a number, any number. Now double that number. Got it? Now add 10 to it. Then, subtract 4…Divide the number you now have by 2. OK, now subtract the number you originally picked. Add 49 to it…And that's the reason there are 52 questions!

1. "It was a cold, bright day in April, and the clocks were striking 13"… So begins what novel by George Orwell?

2. Can you identify the foreign capital named after the fifth U.S. president and the country where it's located?

3. If you were heading south from Detroit, what is the first foreign country you would arrive in?

4. What does NASA stand for?

5. Which state has the longest coastline?

6. How many signs of the Zodiac are there?

According to statistics, a man eats a prune every 20 seconds. I don't know who this man is, but I know where to find him.
-Morey Amsterdam

Illiterates don't have to read this.

7. Which word is mispelled – parallel, embarrass, assassin?

8. What state capital is the southernmost among the 48 contiguous states?

9. National Pi Day falls on what day of March?

10. How many calories does one Hershey's Kisses chocolate contain?

11. The last name is Buonarroti. What's the first name?

12. How many consecutive wins did Ken Jennings have on "Jeopardy" in 2004? a) 34 b) 54 c) 74 d) 104

13. Harry Houdini made his final disappearing act in strangely coincidental fashion. What day did he die?

 The Paul McCartney-written Beatles song "She Came in Through the Bathroom Window" stems from the time a female fan actually crawled through Paul's bathroom window.

14. What does a pogonophobic fear?

15. True or false? Napoleon Bonaparte, a Frenchman, designed the flag of Italy.

16. By what nickname did the world know Robert Stroud?

17. What amendment to the U.S. Constitution abolished slavery?

18. What was the largest denomination of United States currency ever minted?

19. Lexico was the original name of what famous board game?

20. What is the only way to tell a male penquin from a female penquin? (Assuming you're not a penguin)

21. What was the name of the second baseman in Abbott and Costello's "Who's on First?" routine.

I have two brain cells left, and one of them is busy reminding me to buy toilet paper.
-Diana Gabaldon

I need to confront my phobia of German sausages, but I fear the wurst.

22. What age-related issue did First Ladies Martha Washington, Abigail Fillmore, Caroline Harrison, Florence Harding and Pat Nixon have in common?

23. What was the last year that read the same upside down?

24. Which two states have names that come from the Sioux word meaning "friend"?

25. Who is Frank Wills and what small but crucial role did he play in recent American history?

26. Can you name the first U.S. president to play Little League baseball?

27. What vegetable do you discard the outside, cook the inside, eat the outside and chuck the inside?

28. How many teeth does a typical dog have?

29. Who is the only player in Major League Baseball history to legally run the bases backwards after hitting a home run?

30. What does the "L.L." in L.L. Bean stand for?

31. What beverage does the winner of the Indianapolis 500 traditionally drink?

32. What is the longest running prime time network TV program?

33. Which grow faster, your fingernails or your toenails?

34. What is the plural of graffiti?

35. There is only one U.S. state capital that does not share any letters in its name with its state. Can you name it?

36. Miguel Cabrera of the Detroit Tigers won baseball's Triple Crown in 2012. It had been 45 years since the previous winner. Who was that?

37. Do you know the only members of the animal kingdom to commonly sleep on their backs?

Maybe humans are just the pet alligators that God flushed down the toilet.
-Chuck Palahniuk

Boys will be boys,
but girls will be women.

38. What's the only number with its letters in reverse alphabetical order?

39. True or false? There has never been a bachelor president in the United States.

40. What does EPCOT stand for?

41. The time interval "undecennial" means once every how many years?

42. Which state has the most diners in the U.S.?

43. Let's play "Jeopardy!" He was the show's first host, appearing on 1,858 shows between 1964 and 1979. And the question is...?

44. How many feet deep is a twain?

The average American household
keeps eight back-up rolls of
toilet paper on hand.

45. What do the names Chang, Schultz, and Smith have in common?

46. What happens to your social security number when you die?

47. Which heart beats faster: an elephant's or a canary's?

48. What former president's face is on the $2 bill?

49. When he started the American Messenger Company in 1907 in Seattle, Jim Casey was 19 years old. By the end of World War I, his tiny messenger service had grown considerably and he changed its name to what current outfit?

50. How many keys are on a piano?

51. As you look at it, which way does the eagle's head face on the flip side of a quarter?

52. What's the maximum amount of years that a U.S. president may be in office?

I wish we could still cover neighborhood trees in toilet paper without feeling guilty about wasting precious resources.

-E Cards

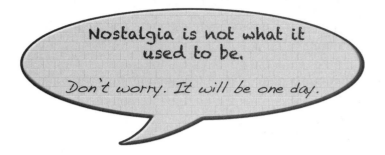

ANSWERS: 1."1984" 2.Monrovia, Liberia 3.Canada
4.National Aeronautics and Space Administration 5.By far, the
state with the longest coastline is Alaska. In fact, its coastline is
longer than that of all the other coastal states combined! Strange
that it never became a beach resort... 6.12 7.You didn't fall for
this, did you? "Mispelled" was misspelled. 8.Austin, Texas 9.March
14- The real "Pi" moments occur March 14, at 1:59 a.m. and
p.m. (3.14159...) 10.25 11.Michelangelo 12.C 13.On Halloween
in 1926 14.A pogonophobic finds beards to be a hair-raising
experience. 15.True 16.One of the most famous residents of "The
Rock," Stroud was known as "The Birdman of Alcatraz." 17.The
Thirteenth Amendment 18.A $100,000 bill, which bore a portrait
of Woodrow Wilson, was the largest denomination. 19.Scrabble
20.By autopsy 21.Hope you didn't try to answer that- look at
it carefully, and you'll see that it's a statement, not a question.
22.They were all older than their husbands. 23.1961 24.North
and South Dakota 25.Wills was the twenty-four-year old security
guard who discovered the Watergate break-in, the
"third-rate burglary" that eventually toppled the Nixon
administration. 26.George W. Bush 27.Corn on the cob
28.42 −20 on top and 22 on the lower jaw 29.Jimmy Piersall −
While playing for the 1963 New York Mets, he did it to celebrate
his 100th career homer. The next day the big league rulebook was
changed to make this illegal. 30.Leon Leonwood (as in Leon

Leonwood Bean, the founder of the store chain) 31.Milk 32.On the air since 1968, it's "60 Minutes," still ticking away after all these years. 33.Thumbs up for your fingernails. They grow about an inch a year, four times faster than your toenails. 34.Graffiti *is* plural. Graffito is singular. 35.Pierre, South Dakota 36.Carl Yastrzemski of the Boston Red Sox, in 1967 37.Human beings 38.1 (O-N-E) 39.James Buchanan, the fifteenth president, was unhitched. 40.Experimental Prototype Community of Tomorrow 41.11 42.New Jersey 43.Who is Art Fleming? 44.12 45.They are the most common last names in China, Germany, and the U.S. respectively. Chang is the most popular name in the world. 46.The numbers are retired, naturally. The nine digit combination gives them about one billion to choose from, so unless we extend benefits to the rest of the world, we have plenty of numbers left. 47.The canary's beats at a much heartier rate – 1,000 times a minute compared to the 27 times per minute of an elephant's heart. 48.Thomas Jefferson 49.United Parcel Service 50.88 – 52 white and 36 black 51.To the left 52.10 – According to the 22nd Amendment to the Constitution, this maximum would be reached by a president completing two years of the term of his/her predecessor, then being elected to two full terms.

I took a baby shower.
-Steven Wright

And now a few closing lines from some of the world's best literature:

"Tomorrow, I'll think of some way to get him back. After all, tomorrow is another day." -"Gone With the Wind" by Margaret Mitchell

• •

"The scar had not pained Harry for nineteen years. All was well." -"Harry Potter and the Deathly Hallows" by J.K. Rowling

• •

"So we beat on, boats against the current, borne back ceaselessly into the past." -"The Great Gatsby" by F.Scott Fitzgerald

• •

"It is a far, far better thing that I do, than I have ever done; it is a far, far better place that I go to than I have ever known." -"A Tale of Two Cities" by Charles Dickens

• •

"This is the end." -"The Bathroom Trivia Companion" by Jack Kreismer